This bo

Children's
POOLBEG

The Lost
City
of Belfast

The Lost City of Belfast

SHAUN TRAYNOR

POOLBEG

First published 1991 by
Poolbeg Press Ltd
Knocksedan House,
Swords, Co Dublin, Ireland.
Reprinted May 1995

Poolbeg Press receives assistance from
the Arts Council / An Chomhairle Ealaíon, Ireland.

ISBN 1 85371 164 0

Cover design and illustrations by Denise Kierans
Set by Richard Parfrey in New Century Schoolbook 13/15
Printed by The Guernsey Press Company Ltd,
Vale, Guernsey, Channel Islands.

Also by Shaun Traynor

Poetry
The Hardening Ground
Images in Winter
Still Life

Essays
The Emancipation of English Poetry in the 20th Century

In Children's Poolbeg
Hugo O'Huge, The Children's Giant
The Giants' Olympics
A Little Man In England

Contents

Contents

Part I

"Don't Forget Your Shovel if You Want to go to Work"

Chapter 1

(In which our hero goes to visit a school where the teacher still uses the cane!)

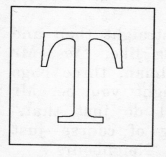his story is about archaeology and if you're wondering how I know what archaeology is, I can tell you. It's because my teacher, Mr Redman, told us what it is. What it is, is digging down and finding things like bones or lost cities and then piecing the bits and pieces together to find out what life was like three thousand years ago or even three hundred years ago. It's just ideal for Belfast!

He has this little joke, Mr Redman: at the end of every day just when we've got our coats on and are sitting nicely ready to go home he always says, "Now on to the subject of archaeology; why don't you all go home and have a little dig in your own gardens tonight: you never know what you might find. It might be that one of you sitting there is a budding archaeologist!"

We sit up really straight then and always say something like, "Yes, Mr Redman, no, Mr Redman, three bags full, Mr Redman, right you be, Mr Redman," and "We'll do just that." Then we do nothing of course—just go home and watch "Neighbours".

Then we go in the next day and say, "Mr Redman, Mr Redman, I dug and I dug but I never found nothing, honest." He will then say, "Don't give up, keep on digging!" Then he does a really crazy thing, he plays a tape of Christy Moore singing and he sings along. These are the words:

Don't forget your shovel if you want to go to work.

This is how he always begins and ends his archaeological lessons and in the middle of a lesson he sometimes breaks into song as well with another line:

You'll never get to heaven if you're always diggin' holes.

Well, obviously not. Obviously our Mr Redman is a real header but I like him—we all do.

Of course there's a serious side to archaeology: it would be great to go on an expedition and find a lost city or something else that's interesting; it would be great to discover something no one ever knew before. The thing about history and books and maps is that you never hear the people speaking or smell them, if you know what I mean. I like films like *Raiders of the Lost Ark*—that was about archaeology—and also *Back to the Future* which was about time-travel. I would love to be in an adventure, in my own block-busting movie. Well, come on now, what's wrong with having a dream?

I live up Cliftonville: Woodland Avenue is my actual address, number

14, the end house. From my bedroom window I can see the waterworks. It's really beautiful, you know, and the nicest thing of all is that every day and at every time of the day you see people throwing crusts of bread to the swans. Belfast people are very kind. The swans are beautiful and there's an awful lot of them, maybe fifty or sixty, so it's a lot to keep fed. When they all take off together or land together it is very thrilling. It's like war: the swans are like war-planes taking off and landing.

One night I was up watching them and my ma and da were watching telly downstairs and I suddenly thought as dusk was falling that maybe I would go out into my back garden and have a dig. It had been magical watching the swans and it made me feel magical and I got to thinking that after all somebody has to be the first to find something and why shouldn't there be something to find in Belfast and why shouldn't it be *me* that finds it?

"That's daft," I thought, but all the same I went downstairs and slipped quietly out the back door and got the shovel from my da's shed. I put on my wellies as well because the ground was wet.

I started digging by the light of the moon and by the light of the stars as those lights came through the branches and leaves of the old next-door tree that nearly covers the garden and makes it a very dark place even in the summer. In the summer the sun can hardly get through the foliage so I mean you'd never get a tan. I dug an area about eight foot square just lifting a little bit of earth at a time at first and then went back over it and got down a bit deeper.

Then I really *did* find something!

❖

At first I couldn't be certain—the light wasn't great—but then as I looked closer I found that I had discovered some stone steps. I could see the moonlight glinting on the damp stone. I got down on my hands and knees and peered thoroughly. There were indeed steps leading down and down and down, and in the darkness there seemed to be no end to them.

I went back inside and got a torch and put on an anorak and then went back out to the hole and started to climb down. The steps went down and down and it was cold and dark until warm air began to blow and it became quite pleasant and a strange kind of light mixed with the darkness and I could see quite easily so I skipped on down a bit further and then I came to a door. It said on it: *Victorian Ireland*. I pushed it open and walked out into sunlight and onto a street in a small town in the north of Ireland.

I knew it was small because I could see the fields that marked the end of it—fields to the north and to the south and to the east; there was a wood to the west. I knew I was in Ulster because of the accents and I knew it was at least a hundred years ago because of the way the people were dressed. They wore old-fashioned clothes and the shops too were very old-fashioned and quaint. It was all very nice but then something awful

happened to me and that's the next bit of the story.

A kind of butterfly net flew over my head and I was captured by an evil-looking man who dragged me off to a pony and trap. He was like the truant catcher out of *Chitty Chitty Bang Bang*, tall and thin and bent and old with a hook nose and eyes that had water streaming out of them. Every so often he would dab at them with a handkerchief as if he had hay fever. But there was no doubt about what he was—a Victorian truant-catcher —and he had caught me!

By looking at the sun I reckoned it must be about mid-morning so that would have been *why* he had captured me. He must have thought I was a wee Victorian child walking about *not at school*. He obviously couldn't have been expected to know that I was from a different time and a different place. Come to think of it (and it was just then that I did start to think about it)—it was one thing to climb down the stone steps and out through a door—*but how was I going to get back?*

He put me in a sack and threw me in the back of the trap. When we got to the school which was not much more that a wee house, he shoved me in the door and shouted to the head-master, "Here's another yin, I'm away out to look for a wheen more!" Off he went and I was left trembling. The master was ranting away about some-thing and swishing a long cane about. I slipped into a vacant seat at the back. Every time he got to the end of a sentence the master would slap his cane on his desk *whack* like a full stop.

I had never seen a cane before although I had heard plenty about them and had seen photographs. Now I was in a room with one and it was in the hand of a very swishy teacher. As he spoke he swished it about here, there and everywhere, and the way he looked at everybody and glowered I felt sure he probably caned somebody every single minute of every single day. He did seem very cruel; also the cane was old and yellow with age and looked as if it had been used lots and lots of times on weeping, frightened children.

The master got on with his lesson. "Last one," he said, so I figured the children must have been doing some kind of quiz or test. "Spell 'The Hague'," he said, so I knew I was right—it was the last word in a spelling test. "Spell 'The Hague'," he repeated and then went on, "and I don't mean the Plague in London, I mean The Hague in Holland where the great King Billy came from." I suddenly knew what the master looked like now, he was like an Orangeman on the Twelfth of July and his belly was like a big Lambeg drum that he carried out in front of him underneath his Presbyterian waistcoat.

He started to go round to look at the answers to the spelling test. As he went round he gave each child a set of marks and a comment, "Marks: six out of ten; comment: no good! marks: seven out of ten; comment: not much better! marks: two out of ten; comment: swish, whack! nought out of ten: hold your hand out; swish, swish

swish; whack, whack, whack!"

"Howl howl howl! Boo-hoo-hoo!"

When he got to me I was shaking with fear.

"Where's your question paper, child?" he shouted.

"I haven't got none," I whispered.

"Where's your pencil, child?" he roared.

"I haven't got none," I replied.

"No pencil, no paper?" he said. "That means no marks: nought out of ten. Hold out your hand," and he swished the cane back. I just got away in time.

When I say "got away," what I mean is I ran as far as the door and then I looked back and shouted, "I'm from a different time and a different place and I think you're horrid; you're cruel and, even worse, you're old-fashioned! You're out of a comic. I wish you were dead. Oh how I wish, how I wish I were back with dear, kind Mr Redman again. I feel sorry for the children in your class!"

He came down the room towards me, cane swishing. I escaped this time all right. I ran through the door and along the road and into the town and through the town and into the wood. Out of breath and still running I saw a strange bird standing by some brambles. It stood proudly and was as tall as any eight- or nine-year-old of us. Did I say strange? The bird was weird! It had the head of a cock and the body of a hen and the claws of an eagle. Also it could speak. It said, "This way, child, this way, child; jump!" I obeyed instructions. I threw myself into the brambles, fingers crossed, praying everything would turn out all right.

"From my red eye you may take a stone," said the strange creature who said he was a cock-a-trice. Another name given to him was a basilisk. He was mythical. (Just the kind of thing you would expect to meet on an archaeological dig.) I took the stone right of out the bird's eyeball. It was as red as a ruby. "Rub the stone if you're ever in trouble," said my new friend. "It will get you back home in no time at all."

"Back home to Belfast?" I asked,

hardly daring to believe my luck.

"Yes indeed," said the cockatrice. "On your many travels, child—and believe me there are many adventures in store for you—you have only to rub this stone which came from the unblinking eye of a basilisk and you will be back in Woodland Avenue, number 14, looking out at the waterworks again." (How did he know that?)

"Thank you, Mr Basilisk, Mr Cockatrice."

"Now child," the strange creature asked, "what's your name?"

I said, "Kate Bruce."

At that the bird stood aside and I could see another door. I went through it and then began my climb back up; back up to bed, to sleep, to school and in the morning to dear old Mr Redman again. Well, on second thoughts, perhaps he's not *that* old.

I ran up the last of the stone steps and on into the house and up to my bedroom. My parents were still watching "Coronation Street" so there must have been a time-trip. All the time I had been away was no time at all on earth.

I went to my window and saw the swans landing like space-ships. They settled, ruffled their feathers, tucked their heads into their wings and went to sleep. The water was still and the moon rode across it like a wee cork boat. Along the street the lamplight flickered. An army patrol passed by noiselessly. Each soldier looked to the north, looked to the south, to the east and to the west, to above him and below him in fear of a sniper.

Chapter 2

(In which Kate tells her story and is taken for a liar.)

s you can imagine, I could hardly wait to get to school to see Mr Redman in the morning to tell him what I had discovered, what I knew. I walked to school past the graffiti, the tanks and the now different soldiers—day-shift, night-shift. I couldn't wait for Mr Redman to arrive but of course as usual he was late. Even when he wasn't late he always waited until we were all seated and then he would walk in and we would have to stand up again; and we would say, "Good morning, Mr Redman," and then we would all sit down again. It was a shocking waste of time but it made him feel good.

Then there was the dinner money
and the register and then a little chat
about Our News to be written first
in our rough books and then eventually
into our News Books. This took us
up to lunchtime. Then it was maths
and then after play in the afternoon,
Story. That was when a few of us,
the day's chosen few, could read the
news they had written to the rest of
the class. It saved Mr Redman from
having to do anything really at the
end of the day.

What I wanted was to be asked to
speak first that morning, to tell
everything, and then to be asked again
at the end of the day when I had
made it all up into a perfect story to
read it. But I wasn't chosen. It was
"fingers-on-lips" for me. What he says
is, "Don't talk; don't spoil it; write it
all down. We'll read it out at the end
of the day, at story-time." Some people
were chosen. Even though it wasn't
Monday they still had weekend things
like, "I went to hospital, visited my
mum, she's having another baby." Or
"I went to the park and played

football. Here's my picture." This is supposed to inspire us, the others! I had *so much* to say! In silence I wrote and this is what I wrote:

Last night Mr Redman I dug down in my back garden like you always said to do and I found some stone steps and I climbed down and I came out into a country town where I was captured by a truant-catcher and made to be a part of an old-fashioned school and there was a man there, the teacher, who had a cane and horrible whiskers and he was going to cane me but I ran away and my life was saved by a cock-a-trice. I hope that I have spelled cock-a-trice right. Another name for it was a baselisk, I hope I have spelled that right. Then I came to school. If you want to hear more choose me at three o'clock to read my news.

Yours, Kate Bruce.

Again I couldn't wait until story-time. I was chosen and when it was my turn I read out my piece. The children were all really interested but Mr Redman said, "A very good story, Kate, but rather a tall one, don't you think?" I couldn't believe it. I said, "It's not made up, Mr Redman; it really happened." Mr Redman said, "I don't believe you, Kate," and then of course all the children started chanting,

I don't believe you;
don't believe you

and I started to cry.

"All right," said Mr Redman, "I'm sorry, Kate. I *don't* believe you but I will apologise if you go down again and bring me a whisker from the teacher's beard and of course *the cane*. When I see the cane, I will believe you."

The children all laughed, thinking I had been well caught out. I smarted with hurt and embarrassment. My hurt was like eczema but I intended to do just what he challenged.

That night I dug down again, heard the strains of Christy Moore mocking me,

Don't forget your shovel
if you want to go to work

and

You'll never get to heaven
if you're always diggin' holes

Well, where I was going might not be heaven—but I intended to prove I had been telling the truth.

Before I left the house that evening of course I packed a torch and some sandwiches but this time I also took a tiny pair of nail-scissors and something very special, a toy, but I shan't tell you which toy it was.

I climbed down again and found the door marked *Victorian Ireland*, pushed it open and found myself on the street again. I ran to the school and into the classroom. The class was in full progress. I had brought things with me but I had also done something I thought rather clever, my surprise and safeguard if you like—I had dressed in a way which would astonish them: I wore a baseball cap, tee-shirt, jeans and trainers. I looked like—and they would know I was—a modern kid.

The girls there of course were all in pinafores, a kind of school uniform, and the boys all wore the same kind of tweed short trousers and little jackets. They all wore men's hats on their boys' heads. When I burst in everyone gasped. Even the horrible little headmaster had now to realise that I came from a different place and a different time.

I put on a real posh Malone Road type of accent and said, "I have brought you a gift from the next century and I have come to receive a gift from you, sir. I want to snip a hair from your hairy whiskers and I want that cane! Hitting children is obscene."

He said to me, "Well, here's our little friend again; what have *you* brought *us* from your time and place?" He also sounded really sarcastic the way too many schoolteachers do. I brought out my toy, a remote-control car, and set it down on the floor and working the controls I made it spin all round the place. It was as if a mouse or a rat or a lion had been let loose—all the boys and girls (the headmaster too) leapt up onto their desks as if this seemingly magic thing was going to attack them. Well, it wasn't actually a car, it was a tank. I didn't tell them what it was, they just saw a thing moving round and thought I was a witch or a wizard or something like that. There was pandemonium!

When order was restored the master said, "You want my hair as Delilah once asked of Samson, and you want the cane from my hand? Very well, we challenge you to a competition, winner take all. Can you spell?" I said I could. He said, "Bring forward Briony; she is our best speller. We challenge you to a spelling test! If you win you can have what you desire."

Briony and I sat down together— well, not together, a desk or so apart so there would be no chance of copying

and the test began—it was the same
kind of words as before: William,
Twelfth of July, Roman Catholic,
Protestant...
The test paper looked like this:

Briony

William	*orange*	*Lambeg*
switch	*cathlic*	*dram*
Londonderry		*Athlone*
water	*amusement*	

Kate

William	*orange*	*Lambeg*
switch	*cathlic*	*dram*
Londonderry		*Athlone*
water	*amusement*	

At the end it was a tie: nine out of ten, nine out of ten.

Then I said, "OK, let's have a tie-breaker and for the tie-breaker, since you've picked words from your time, now I'll pick words from my time and we'll see who gets it right."

"Agreed," said the others.

I had thought of *supercalifragilistic-expialidocious,* but then I thought of a better one, *remote-control car.* The test began: I got it right because I remembered the spelling from the box the car had come in, but Briony wrote, *remoat controll cart.*

The reason for this was of course that she would never have heard of a remote-control car. What Briony would have heard of was a *moat* which is water surrounding a castle, she would have heard of a *troll*, the ugly dwarf in "The Three Billy-goats Gruff" and of course she would have heard of a cart but not a *motor*-car because they weren't even invented then. I had won. Indeed I had won but more important, I became friends with Briony. Then I claimed my prize. I snipped a little hair from his ear and then took the cane.

This time everyone said cheerio and I plunged back into the woods rubbing my red eye-stone. A door opened and I was back on the damp stone steps that led to Belfast. Up and up I went until I came to the garden of number 14 and on up to my room and safe and sound in bed. I could hardly wait for morning to come.

The next day I brought to school the cane from Victorian Ireland and the little bit of hair which I had wrapped in an envelope. At news time I showed them to Mr Redman. The children were silent, waiting to hear what he would say. He looked for a moment, then said, "You could have got the hair from your da's beard and the cane from a museum." The class sniggered. "On to work," said Mr Redman but I did notice he looked a little perplexed.

I felt very hurt, I had done everything my teacher had asked but he still didn't believe me. He thought I was a liar. I put the cane on the history and geography table and the hair on the science table. I felt I had done enough for one day. It was especially unjust because my da doesn't even have a beard! He *hates* beards!

denise '91

Part II

The Famine

Chapter 3

(In which our Kate decides to dig for herself and discovers another part of Ireland's history and also meets a famous poet.)

I was a bit fed up with what had happened at school so that night I decided to dig down just for myself. Because I had decided to go further this time I took some extra big sandwiches and a flask of lemonade. I went down and down, past the door marked *Victorian Ireland* and then almost immediately—not all that much further down—was another door marked *The Famine*. "That would be a good place for the sandwiches," I thought and opened it and found myself in a bog. It was the most desolate place I had ever seen or could have imagined. Suddenly it wasn't a joke any more.

31

The sky overhead was grey and broken and it was raining, raining as if a stable roof was caving in; the land was purple and brown and green and wet and people moved slowly and awkwardly across it as if they had a load on their backs or had webbed feet or were walking on tennis racquets. They were looking for potatoes but the potatoes had the blight—they were dying of hunger. They were wailing and moaning and kind of chanting, "No potaties, no good food in the ground!" They were crying; tears were falling everywhere.

I saw one group of people who seemed like a family: a once-fat mother wearing a short-sleeved frock she once would have been bursting out of but now it hung on her as if she were a coat-hanger. With her were her children; there were seven of them and they were dressed in rags. They were really dirty, really filthy and they moved nearly on all fours like dogs or hyenas. She lumbered along after them or waddled in the middle of them. She was a bit like a baby elephant, swinging her arms out in front of her like a trunk and making a loud moaning noise a bit like an exhausted trumpet. When they saw me they shuddered and moved close together like a pack as if they were frightened. Then they moved towards me very, very suspiciously, peering at me and rubbing their eyes as if they couldn't believe what they saw; closer and closer they came to me. It was me that was frightened now—of these half-humans.

They began to speak, first of all amongst themselves, then to me. They spoke in Irish:

Who is she, what is she,
What, what have we here?
Who are you, child, where have
    you come from,
What, oh what, are you doing
    here?

I said, "My name is Kate, I mean you no harm, I don't speak Irish, can you speak English?" I held out my hand. They muttered again in Irish, then the woman spoke in a heavily brogued English, "We don't like to speak the language of our masters. My name is Martha and these are seven of my children. The other seven are in England begging with their father, a good man, a good, good man who's far away." Then she began to cry and all the children began to cry and it was like a lament.

I opened my little haversack and took out my lemonade and sandwiches. We shared them. Martha and her family ate ravenously and make a little circle round me.

Then we heard a bugle sound and the tap of a drum and over the hill a straggly line of soldiers appeared carrying urns and big spoons. "Come and get your soup," they cried, "and see how England loves you!" The old woman in a sudden fury ran to the roadside and shook her fist at them and shouted, "We want none of your English soup, so climb a tree!" The soldiers laughed as they passed on their way and shouted back, "You'll be on your knees tomorrow, Mad

Martha, and that's when we might pass you by."

"Go climb a tree!" she shouted again and as I took a step forward to watch more of the drama I stepped into something squelchy and unpleasant. I looked down at my shoe and saw that I had stepped into an old squelchy, mushy, stinking, rotten potato. I picked up another small one that was lying beside it and put it in my pocket, not as a souvenir, because this wasn't like a holiday, but just as a kind of memento as to what this part of Irish history was all about.

I then said goodbye and rubbed the red stone plucked from the eye of my basilisk and disappeared. As I slowly dissolved I saw their amazed faces and I saw them fall to their knees. I suppose they thought I was Our Lady or something.

I found myself back in the Tunnel of Time with its own strange light and as I made my way homeward I met an old, kind-looking man. He had a droopy white moustache and he stooped and whispered to me. "You can't go home yet," he said. "There is much, much more to see of this part of Ireland's history. Do you know what emigration is?" he asked mischievously.

I said, "I don't."

"Well, I'll tell you," he says. "An emigrant is someone who emigrates, now do you get it?"

I said I did not for it was obvious that if I didn't know what emigration was how could I know what emigrate meant or what an emigrant was. Not wanting to appear totally stupid, I said an emigrant sounded rather like the name of a bird.

"How clever you are, child," he said, "and how much more there is for you to learn." He ushered me to another door that had on it the sign of a ship. He opened it and I passed through it alone.

I found myself in Queenstown by a quayside. There were thousands of people milling about all trying to board the one ship.

"Only a hundred more," cried the captain of the ship. "Only ninety more," cried the captain again. "Only forty more," now was his cry and then, "twenty places left now, all aboard, all aboard and off to America, Americay, Americay..."

Just at that moment a young man grabbed me up and sprang aboard the ship ahead of the queue. I looked up startled and saw he was brown-haired, brown-eyed, about seventeen and fit and strong but very thin. "We'll stow away," he said, "start a new life away from this sad, sad country that is pillaged by hunger and by plague."

In the noise and bustle I couldn't make myself heard to explain that I hadn't intended going anywhere except back home. Now, not only was I miles from home, I was also years away and I just hoped my basilisk's eye-stone would save me—would work at sea or in America.

That night we found ourselves in a crowded cabin. Finbar, which was the name of my new friend, was very sad. Tears were beginning in his eyes. I asked him what was wrong and he said he was home-sick and wanted to write a letter home. I said to him,

"Why don't you?"

He said, "I cannot read nor write; I'm no good to anybody."

I told him not to worry and again the tears welled up in his brown eyes. I told him I could read and write and I would write the letter for him if he would tell me what to say.

"I dunno what to say," he said when I had set the paper and pencil on the table.

"Well, what do you think you want to say?" I asked patiently.

"I dunno," he said dolefully.

"Who do you want to write to?" I asked.

"Danny," he said.

"All right," I said and began to write.

Dear Danny,
I'm taking the pen in my hand to tell you...

I waited for him to speak:

We're just out of sight of the land

denise 91

Then there was a pause, then:

*In the grand Allen liner we're
sailin' in style
But we're sailing away from the
Emerald Isle.*

He now warmed to his task:

*And a long sort of sigh seemed
to rise from us all
As the waves hid the last bit of
ould Donegal
Och! it's well to be you that is
takin' yer tay
Where they're cuttin' the corn in
Creeshla the day.
I spoke to the captain—he won't
turn her round
And if I swum back I'd be apt
to be drowned,
So here I must stay—oh! I've
no cause to fret...*

Here he stopped again and sat
silent. After a while I asked him what
was the matter. He said, "I miss
Katey."

"Who's she?" I asked.

"My girl-friend," he replied. He
thought for a while, then he said (and
I wrote down):

If Katey is courted by Patsey or
  Mick,
Put a word in for me with a
  lump of a stick...
For Katey might think that the
  longer she waits,
A boy in the hand is worth
  two in the States.

Then he said,

Goodbye to you, Dan, there's no
  more to be said
And I think the salt water has
  got to my head.

"What do you mean?" I asked.

It drips from my eyes when I
  call to my mind
The friends and the colleen I'm
  leaving behind.
Oh, Danny, she'll wait, when I
  bid her goodbye,

*There was just the last taste of
a tear in her eye,
And a break in her voice when
she said, "You might stay,
But please God you'll come back
to ould Creeshla some day."*

*Love
Finbar*

I could bear it no longer. I rubbed the hard, red stone I had taken from the eye of my cockatrice and I was back in the time-tunnel.

I started to climb up the steps and I met the kindly old gentleman again.

"Where have you been?" he asked.

"On a ship," I said excitedly, "and I met an emigrant and he wrote a letter!"

He took from the pocket of his tall frock-coat a book. It said on the cover, *The Poems of Percy French*. He opened it and on the first page there was a poem called "The Emigrant's Letter". He turned over the page. On the next page was the title of a poem, "The Mountains of Mourne", but no words beneath it. He leafed through the rest

of the book. All the pages were blank.
"Come with me," he said, "and we'll
write this poem together."

Off we went through a door marked
The Mountains of Mourne and found
ourselves in the middle of London,
in Piccadilly Circus! I would have
thought we would have arrived in
Newcastle which is where the
Mountains of Mourne are but then
it is not for me, perhaps, to ask such
questions.

So here we were in the hustle and
bustle, the hurly-burly of the busiest
part of London waiting to cross the
road. He had me by the hand. All of
a sudden he shouted out, "Kate, look,
there's yer man!"

I looked to where he was pointing.

"That's just a policeman," I said.

"That's *not* just a policeman," he
insisted, "that's yer man, Peter
O'Loughlin. Come on!" He charged
across the busiest street in London
trailing me after him.

"Peter, Peter," he shouted. "'Bout ye!"

The policeman turned and when he
saw Mr French he gave a delighted

shout. "Percy!" he shouted. "'Bout ye, ould han'," and the two of them stood there talking for ages. I only heard bits of their conversation because of the tooting of the traffic but I did hear Constable McLoughlin say during their exchanges, "The money's good, Percy, but I miss the ould sod and the crack by the sea, the swimming and the walks in summer and, of course, herself."

Constable McLoughlin kept one hand up and for the whole time they were talking no traffic could move; it was really embarrassing!

When they'd finished their chat Mr French took me on a bus tour of the city. It was in an open bus, one with no roof, and we sat on top, up at the front, and saw the whole of London.

Going past Buckingham Palace we saw the king and the whole bus cheered, all the people. Mr French cheered as well and so did I. It was very thrilling. Then we went to the Savoy to have afternoon tea. It was here that Mr French began writing his poem. I was able to watch him and sometimes he spoke to me as well. This is what he wrote:

> *I seen England's King from the*
> *   top of a 'bus—*
> *I never knew him though he*
> *   means to know us:*
> *And though by the Saxon we*
> *   once were oppressed,*
> *Still I cheered—God forgive*
> *   me—I cheered wid the rest.*
> *And now that he's visited Erin's*
> *   green shore*
> *We'll be much better friends*
> *   than we've been heretofore;*
> *When we've got all we want,*
> *   we're as quiet as can be*
> *Where the Mountains of Mourne*
> *   sweep down to the sea.*

He had a sip of tea, smiled and went on, reading out to me as he wrote,

> *You remember young Peter*
> *   O'Loughlin of course—*

*Well, here he is now at the
    head of the Force.
I met him today, I was crossin'
    the Strand
And he stopped the whole street
    with one wave of his hand.
And there we stood talking of
    days that are gone
While the whole population of
    London looked on:
But for all these great powers,
    he's wishful like me,
To be back where dark Mourne
    sweeps down to the sea.*

I said to him, "Excuse me, Mr French,
but we weren't crossing the Strand
when we saw Constable O'Loughlin, we
were in Piccadilly Circus."

"Hm," he said.

"And another thing," I said—

"No more things!" he said. "There
is such a thing as poetic licence, you
know!"

I didn't know but I decided not to
press the matter. I imagined it was
something like a driving licence, a
licence of some sort that allows you

to do something other people can't do. In the case of poets perhaps to make mistakes.

To tell you the truth I was a bit hurt that he had written,

> *I met him today, I was crossing the Strand...*

because it should have been,

> *We met him today, we were crossing the Strand...*

or

> *Kate and I met him today, we were crossing the Strand...*

I felt a bit left out.

Just then the waitress came back with more tea. She was very attractive and I saw old Mr French's eyes sparkle. Just for badness, I put my hand in my school-coat pocket and rubbed the magic stone. Mr French landed right back in the couch as if he had been hit by a cushion and disappeared.

We met again, moments later, in the dark of the stone steps, down in his part of the time tunnel. When our eyes became accustomed to the half-light or strange-light, he showed me his book again. There were two poems in it now, fully written, "The Emigrant's Letter" and "The Mountains of Mourne."

He gave me the book as a gift as he said goodbye.

As I trudged back up the steps, step after step, so the book began to fill up with others of Mr French's poems not written at the time I had met him. So with each step which might have been a month or a year, different poems were written. By the time I got to the final step the book was finished.

I will never part with it.

That night the swans were uneasy in the water. I couldn't sleep either and I was up and down all night watching them as they shifted and irritably pecked at each other in their failure to get to sleep.

Part III
The Siege of Derry

Chapter 4

(In which Kate finds a warning blowing in the wind.)

y da was having his tea one night. I think he had been to the pub on his way home because of the way he was eating his fry. Egg was dribbling down his chin and he ate it as if he were starving. Anyway he asked me through mouthfuls what I had been doing at school that day. I said we had done some maths and he asked me what five times five was and I said twenty-five and that was the maths taken care of.

Then I said that after that we started learning about the Famine. At this point he seemed to choke a bit but he did keep the bit of bacon in his mouth. Then he said, "What are

you studying *that* for? What you *should* be studying is the great Siege of Derry. That's when people were *really* starving," and he poked his dripping knife in the air at me as if to make the point.

"I'm going to write a letter to that school," he said, "and tell your precious, fiddley-daddley Mr Redman not to be teaching you Catholic history but to teach you Protestant history. The Siege of Londonderry is the stuff of hunger, not the Famine." He got up from the table and got a bit of paper and a pencil and wrote this letter:

> *14 Woodland Ave*
> *Belfast 14*
> *24.4.91*

Dear Mr Redman,
I am shocked that a good Unionist like yourself should be teaching my Kate things about the Famine which might be anti-British propaganda. There's a lot of propaganda in that episode that is still used against England. If you want to teach about hunger, what you

should be teaching her is the Siege of Londonderry where we stood alone against James and his hordes.

Yours sincerely,
Philip Bruce

This I had to take to school and did. Mr Redman read it and smiled. "Indeed," he said, "your da has a point. It wasn't my intention to teach just the Famine. I do intend to investigate the Siege of Derry and then later in the summer term to have our project on the Battle of the Boyne. Tell your da that, Kate, and tell him he can come in any time and have a chat with me about you if he wants. We should maybe talk about the time-climbing."

I had in a way lost faith in school because everyone—and especially Mr Redman—was being so sarcastic to me, so I decided to say nothing to anybody this time but climb down and find out what I could *for myself* and keep it all in my head. That very night I began the descent.

I was tired when I got to the right door. It had taken much longer than before so I knew I was further back in time. I had passed many doors before I came to an old oak one that said on it *The Siege of Derry*. It creaked as I opened it and it was very heavy as I pushed it against earth and time. I finally got it open and went through and found myself, not in Derry at all, but in a wee town somewhere else altogether. Then I realised it was Comber for there was a sign over a smithy which said *J Kennedy, Blacksmith, Comber.*

It was snowing. Inside the smithy looked red and warm. Outside it was very, very cold. There was a bitter wind blowing and there was no one about. I was glad I had a coat on and I turned the collar up. I was walking up the main street wondering what this place had to do with the Siege of Derry when suddenly I was hit in the face by a big piece of wet paper like a page from a newspaper. I pulled it off my face and looked to see what it was. It was a letter, a warning. In a way it was like the warning given to the Jews before the Passover, only this time it wasn't to the Jews that a warning was being given—it was to the Protestants.

I read it in astonishment. It was a warning to Protestants that there was a plot to kill them and they must flee to a place of safety. I wanted to throw it away in case I interfered with the course of history but I couldn't do that because I was now a part of it. The warning was dated December, 1688.

I desperately wondered what to do. I ran back to the smithy and showed it to the blacksmith. He couldn't read but he got someone else who could and who immediately realised how important the warning was (thank goodness!) and gathered round him all the important people of the town and showed them the letter, saying, "Barricade yourselves in your homes tonight and to those unhappy people in this town who have no homes or who are just passing through, may I say, get to somewhere safe before nightfall."

Then I heard people telling each other, whispering at first and then speaking more excitedly, "We'll go to Derry! Even though it's a good bit away. Get behind the walls of Derry, we'll be safe there! Get behind the walls of Derry!"

Since the reader of the letter had mentioned people who were "passing through," I reckoned that could definitely mean *me* and I joined the crowd. The next thing I knew was that I was in front of one of Derry's gates in a scene of great turmoil. The governor, Colonel Lundy, was arguing with just about everybody else as to whether or not he should shut the gates. It seemed a bit daft to me if an enemy were coming to leave them open—but later it was explained to me that the enemy who was coming was in fact King James, the legal king of Ireland, so if you shut the gates against him you would be committing treason and could be hanged.

Nevertheless most people in Derry wanted to shut the gates against

James and his Catholic army. They hoped a Protestant king might come. Lundy warned that if anyone came against James, there would be a civil war.

I showed Governor Lundy the letter I had found. He looked really shocked when he read it. Then someone grabbed it from him and read it out. That did it! Suddenly the cry went up from the watch. Tyrconnell's army had crossed the Foyle. A crowd of young lads, apprentices with the London companies, rushed forward and shut the gates. At that same moment, the first shot against them was fired. The siege had begun.

Chapter 5

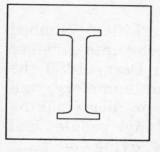

t was funny having been in at the start of the Siege of Derry in real life and then to come back to the classroom and hear Mr Redman's account of it. It wasn't the same at all. He never mentioned the letter I had found in Comber but he did tell us about Colonel Lundy getting away from the citizens dressed as a woman and carrying tinder on his back. I hadn't seen that. I had left before it had happened.

Governor Lundy had got away all right but only because he was dressed as a match-lady; that is why we Protestants burn an effigy of him every year to remind ourselves of how

59

close we came—and all because of him—to giving Derry to James in the winter of 1688. It was only my letter, the Comber letter, that had saved the day.

It was spring when I next climbed down. Spring was turning into summer in Belfast 1991 but in Derry 1689 the weather was far from summery and there was no singing or merrymaking behind the walls. Many people had died there and were dying of starvation. I knew now what my da had meant when he talked about hunger.

It was a child's birthday. She was one of the daughters of the family I was staying with. Her name was Roseanne but she never spoke to me. She kept her head down all the time. For her birthday there were no candles and no cake. The family had a barbecue. They roasted a rat on a spit and then shared it out little bit by little bit. I'll never forget the sight or taste or feel of that wee hunched-up, finger-burning, lark-like, roasted thing being torn apart by people on the verge of death by starvation.

Worse was to come. When I say "worse" what I really mean is "more revolting."

The family I was staying with went—I suppose you would have to call it shopping—on the following Monday morning for food for a week and I went with them. There was a big sign at the butcher's of things that you could buy; this is what it said:

Roll up Roll up

1/4 dead dog (fed on Irishman)
5s 6d

a dead dog's head   2s 6d

a cat (Sunday lunch)   4s 6d

a rat   1s 0d

a mouse   0s 6d

I won't tell you what the family bought!

On the way out of the shop the

old granny of the house whispered to me, with tears in her eyes, "If things go on like this, Kate, we'll be eating each other one day!" I could believe her, for in Spain today, in the twentieth century, they eat larks, in France they eat snails, and we, ourselves, eat lambs and pigs and gentle cows.

As we walked back home a cannonball landed at our feet. It was a spent one and in it was a message. It was a last request from King James and his men for us to give up. He promised that no one would be punished and that if we were Protestants we would be allowed to remain Protestants and come to no harm. That seemed fair enough to me but the older people in the city told me the same things had been promised in England but never carried out. "King's promises," they said, "are made to be broken."

So it was that the people of Derry, even though they were starving, decided not to give in, not to surrender. They wrote to King William in London asking him to come and help them, to march now against the Catholic James. No one then could have guessed how much history would be changed by William's coming to Ulster.

I had not forgotten about what granny-in-the-house had said that one day we might eat ourselves and so I was very frightened when I heard this song some kids on the street were singing; they were chanting the words and two of them were drumming on two little drums. They sang and whispered,

> *Where's the fat-boy, where's the fat-boy,*
> *fat-boy, fat-boy your time has come;*
> *we'll eat your skin and boil your bone*
> *and after that we'll roast your fat;*
> *for a treat we'll burn it brown,*
> *roast your fat and burn it brown;*

*Fat-boy, fat-boy your time has
come.*
*Fat-boy, fat-boy we'll boil your
eyes,*
*peel your shins and fork your
thighs,*
*fat-boy, fat-boy your time has
come.*

Who could they mean?

When I got home that night I heard this weak voice calling from next door, "Kate, Kate, help, help!" I remembered there was a fat man living there, I remembered even more now: he lived on his own! So it wasn't "boy" they meant, it was "man!" Of course! He would just be the one to start on!

I went round and right enough it was him. He was hiding away in a cupboard. He had been there for days! "I'm so scared, Kate," he said, "so scared. Can you get me a cup of water?"

I went to bed that night sick at heart, feeling guilty even, that it was so easy for me just to time-trip away, while all these other people had to

Denise '91

stay and suffer, Protestants and
Catholics too.

Chapter 6

t school I think Mr Redman was running out of steam for he started asking me had I any contributions to make. He would ask things like had I time-climbed the night before. When he asked this type of question the class would really sit up ready for a bit of crack but I didn't co-operate. I remained aloof and would contribute nothing.

I let this go on for a day or two, enjoying my aloofness, but then I could stand it no longer. In truth I was bursting to tell them what I knew; so the next time I was asked I stood up and told them all quite seriously about what I had seen and learnt. I told them everything. It took almost an hour.

At the end of it all there was silence, no jokes, just silence. One or two of them had their mouths still open in amazement long after I had stopped talking. This time Mr Redman didn't say, "I don't believe you, Kate, you're telling lies."

He sat for a long while with his chin in his hands, thinking. Then he said, "I want to believe you, Kate, I respect you—we all do, but I can't believe you, Kate, until..." and here he paused and thought very hard again. Then he made his mind up and continued, "—until you bring me back the cannonball that landed at your feet asking the people of Londonderry to surrender.

"Also as a final test find out for me what part a Colonel Clancarty played in the whole affair." He said this last one as if it were the most difficult question in the world. Maybe it would prove so.

That then was the challenge.

That very night I climbed down

again and found myself on the streets of Derry but to my amazement, after a three hour climb—*not in the past!*

I had climbed down all right—you lose count of the steps after about a thousand—I had climbed down with one thought in mind, to find the cannonball and its historic message, but here I was in *the present day*. I couldn't understand it!

The way the steps work is this: you climb down further and further depending on how far back you want to go in time and there are "marker doors," marking important events. To locate smaller events you have to get the time in history roughly right and then *think*, kind of *sense* your way to the right exit. Me now being in the present day was too totally wrong for it not to be some kind of mistake!

It was a Friday and I was in a cathedral. I was in St Columb's Cathedral in Derry, standing in front of a showcase and there was the shell! I recognised it. Then I understood! Suddenly I understood why I hadn't been able to go back in time to find the cannonball. It had been found by someone else and brought back to this, I suppose, kind of shrine.

It was marked, "Cannonball found in Derry with the terms of surrender." I could have laughed out loud at the way my time-tunnel had tricked me and yet both of us had been right all along.

I moved out of the cathedral, crossed myself out of respect, then rubbed the red, hard stone from the eye of the basilisk.

I found myself back on the stone steps at the same point I had exited, at the Siege of Derry time. I searched and searched for the word "Clancarty" amongst the doors but couldn't find it. Not wanting to lose the second of my challenges I went through the door marked *Siege of Derry*, thinking "Clancarty," and hoping against hope to find something "Clancarty-ish." I didn't have long to wait. There came a tremendous knock at the gate.

"Who's there?" asked the guards.

"Colonel Clancarty," replied a man's voice.

"Well, you can't come in," said the guards.

A skirmish began and then Clancarty went away again.

I wondered why Mr Redman had sent me back for this one, why he had treated this one as the fifty thousand dollar question; not a lot happened when you come to think about it. It wasn't long before I found out why.

In class the next day Mr Redman asked me had I found the shell. I said I had and that it was in the cathedral in Derry. Mr Redman again looked serious. Then he asked, "And what about Clancarty?"

"I did time-trip," I said. "I was in Derry and Colonel Clancarty came knocking at the gate but he never got in."

"That's true," said Mr Redman excitedly. "It is an ancient Irish prophecy, that a Clancarty should one day knock on the gates of Derry and not gain admittance! Hardly anybody knows that! Hardly anybody, I mean, of your age ..." His voice began to falter away and he stopped being excited. He realised that by my getting it right he had to decide again whether to believe me or not.

But all he said was, "Thank you for your contributions this term, Kate. Next term's project, children, is the Battle of the Boyne. It's a *book* study, Kate, so you stay home at night!"

Everybody laughed. He had belittled me.

I did stay at home, in fact, lots of nights. I sat on my da's knee and he read to me and my ma made tea off the range and we had lovely suppertimes. Sometimes my da cooked and I helped him and my ma did other wee jobs. One night my da asked, "Did Mr Redman ever get my letter?"

I said he did.

"And what did he say?" my da asked.

"Next term's project is about the Battle of the Boyne."

"Is it? That's sticking out!" Da said and we all went to bed that night very happy indeed.

SHORT
STORIES

Denise '91

Part IV

The Battle of the Boyne

(In which Kate meets King Billy, travels with him from Torbay to London, guides him to the shores of Carrickfergus, then on to Belfast and finally to the Battle of the Boyne.)

Chapter 7

(In Holland)

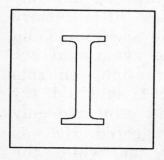n the summer term our project was indeed the Battle of the Boyne. This was suitable for the national curriculum attainment targets because it included history and geography and invasions. It also included maths as we had to measure the distance from Belfast to Dublin, a million miles I think sometimes, but actually it's only ninety-six.

This wasn't as interesting as archaeology but then that's what the national curriculum is for: to stop teachers like Mr Redman teaching what they really enjoy teaching—like archaeology morning, noon and night— and making them teach what someone higher up than them says is good for us kids. Now it all comes from facts and not just from Mr Redman's "sense" of events.

When he saw me yawning one day he said, "Oh dear, our little history expert is bored, maybe she should dig down her stone steps again and see if she can shed more light on this matter than I can." I said I'd try and Mr Redman looked grim and only a few in the class sniggered. He was getting fed up with me while the others were—I have to say it— becoming impressed. If what I was telling them wasn't true, how on earth could I have invented all the things I had told them? Homework? Mr Redman put the tin hat on it when he said, "Maybe if you meet King Billy on your travels you could ask him if he has a message for Mr Paisley?" That did it: I was determined to go.

That night I dug down again. Again I took some sandwiches because I knew it would be a long way and I liked leaving crumbs for the worms and other ancient creepie-crawlies.

I passed the door that said *Victorian Ireland*, went past the wee door that said *The Famine*, past the door that said *The Siege of Derry* and on down until I came to a sign which said simply, *The Battle of the Boyne*. I opened it and found myself in Holland, in The Hague, of all places!

I was in the private apartments of Prince William and his young wife, Mary. I wasn't noticed at first because I found myself on a wee stool behind a beautiful screen which was woven with peacocks in a background of orange, purple and blue. I peeked round and could see the couple quite clearly. They were really young—he was in his early twenties but she looked only about fifteen or so. They sat on two small thrones and were talking. Then they started to pace about. He was really small, much smaller than his wife!

I duked back again out of sight for a wee while but listened. They were having a row. Prince William said, "Mary, your da is King of England

and therefore he should be a Prod, but we all know he's a Catholic and always will be a Catholic and with him England will also become Catholic unless somebody goes and tries to sort it out."

She then replies, "Oh, I don't know what to do, Billy, for the best—I really don't."

"Well, I'll tell you," he says. "I have here some letters from some very important people in England—Protestants—who want me to be their Protestant king."

"But how can you be king, darling?" asked Mary. "If anything happened to daddy, sis or I would be queen and I don't know what that would make you."

"A consort," said William bitterly. He went on, "That is something I will never be. I *must* be king because if you were queen, *would you want to put your da to death?*"

"Oh, no," Mary said, "I couldn't do anything like that. Could you?"

"No," William said, "I like the oul fella but one of us will have to do it unless..."

"Unless what?" Mary asked.

"I dunno," William said and he blew out his lips and looked really miserable.

From this conversation I learnt for the first time that Mary's da was King James, who would be on the Roman Catholic side at the Battle of the Boyne and that she was married to King Billy who would be on the Protestant side. Mr Redman had never told us that King Billy was married to King James's daughter. I felt really sorry for her, loving her father and loving her husband. She was really caught in the middle. That's what I mean about coming underground, you learn so much more and it's all so *interesting*.

"The very best thing to do," Mary said at last, "is for me to write to daddy and tell him you're going to make war on him or something heavy like that...then if he's any sense at all he can get out of England and go to France or somewhere out of the road and we can all meet up later."

"Would you?" William asked. "That

would be brilliant. Go on ahead."

Princess Mary then went to a little bureau and sat down and wrote a letter. She read it out:

House of Orange
Wednesday

Dear Daddy,

William is in a very bad mood, so am I. We're very annoyed you are going to make England a Catholic country once again. Haven't we been through enough? A lot of your own people are annoyed with you too and they want William to come and send you packing—then we will have a proper, Protestant England again.

Neither William nor I want to go to these extremes but if we do come to fight the Catholics, William has asked please, please, please will you get off-side and not get in the road for William (and I, my dearest) would be heart-broken if anything happened to you,

Much love,

Your affectionate daughter
Mary

PS I know you have never forgiven me for marrying a Prod but then the path of true love never does run smooth and I love William.

She then called a footman and they sent the letter. William stood up on a wee footstool and kissed his wife. Then he said, "I love you too. What will be will be."

I just wished a big hole in the ground would open up to let me escape. Then I remembered my stone from the basilisk's eye. I rubbed it just as William and Mary were climbing up into their four-poster bed. Suddenly I disappeared.

The next day at school at project time, I told Mr Redman what had happened. He looked thoughtful. Then he said, "You're trying to tell me that King Billy's da-in-law was King James? That it was all in the family?"

I said that was what I had discovered.

He said, "You've been to the library again, haven't you?"

I said, "Sooner or later, dear Mr

Redman, you will have to learn to trust the wisdom of the wet stone steps."

"What happened next?" he asked.

"Tonight I will time-climb again," I said, "and fill you in tomorrow."

The class went "Ha! Ha!" But I think it was at him for the first time and not at me.

That night in bed I chanted,

Mr Redman, Mr Redman,
I'm not a bookworm,
I'm an earthworm,
So there!

The next night was my birthday so my ma and da had a party for me. Da was in good form and let me bring round all the kids from my class that I wanted. He and ma sorted out food and a cake with eight candles on it. We all blew eight times as balloons whizzed about the room. As each candle went out I remembered the child's birthday-party in Derry, the child who didn't speak and the little roasted rat that was her supper.

Our whole house was full of laughter and high jinks. We were allowed up all the stairs, into all the rooms. And food? Jelly, crisps, sausage-rolls, you name it! It was a wheaker!

We all got overtired, of course, and I was glad that night to see the swans well settled. I decided to get up really early and go and feed them the party scraps before I went to school in the morning.

It was some days before I could pick up again on how King Billy came to England. How he came to Ireland seemed ages away! Maybe through a different door?

Chapter 8

(In England)

hings were quiet for a while. Mr Redman was off sick. We had a supply teacher. She gave us worksheets and wouldn't let us move. My da was on a short shift. I held my breath as far as history was concerned.

I got down again in a few nights' time and came to the door marked *The Battle of the Boyne*, pushed it open and came out in England!

I was on a country road, the air was tangy so I knew I was near the sea and the weather was sunny and chilly. There were no leaves on the trees. Over a hill came a man on a white horse; he looked well-off, was young and had long curly hair but was dressed in old-fashioned soldier's clothes.

I spoke to him, saying, "Good-morning."

He said, "Good-morning," back. Then he said, "Child, do you know the road to London?"

I said I didn't, that I had only just arrived there. I didn't like to say how!

I still didn't recognise him and I asked him was he going up to London to shop.

This made him laugh and he said, "I go shopping for the English crown. I am Prince William of Orange and I am to be the next king of England."

I gasped because I now knew he had set out on his journey into history.

"Are you all alone?" I asked.

"Not alone," he said and waved an arm. Over a hill came thousands of soldiers all on horseback. "I have brought a little army with me and with the army comes my wife."

"Mary?" I said without thinking.

"Yes," he said, surprised. "How did you know that?"

I said I had learnt it at school.

He said, "Tonight we march on London and upon the court of King James. Do you want to come?"

I said I did, that it would be better than school, and he laughed. What he didn't know was that I knew rightly where he had come from and where he was going and that the Boyne was still a long way away.

At that moment three men came running over the fields shouting, "Prince William, Prince William, we have caught King James trying to escape, we have him here with us."

Prince William looked very annoyed. "Who are you?" he asked.

"We are but poor fishermen," the men said. "We were mending our nets when we saw this sleekit old fella trying to climb into one of our boats."

At this we saw King James who stood there very shamefaced.

"Let him go," said Prince William, "I will deal with him personally."

William now got off his horse and walked down to the beach with King James. I couldn't hear what they were saying but I saw James get into a

denise '91

boat and row off to somewhere—France, maybe.

Because I had read the history of their future I thought it very ungrateful and really rather bad of King James to come back again having been let off the once.

William went back and paid the fishermen with a silver coin each and said to them, "Next time you mend your nets, make sure you pay attention to your nets *and nothing else.*"

With that he swooped me up onto the saddle of his white horse where I sat in front of him and so we rode to London.

London was very, very busy. Of course there weren't any buses or cars—there weren't even proper streets! There were, however, coaches. Again, everybody was dressed in different kinds of clothes and there were bears on chains and jugglers and pickpockets, murderers and thieves— at least some of them looked as if they could have been. There were princes and princesses too, a palace and a court but not Buckingham Palace—that hadn't even been built yet!

On my short ride to the centre of town I saw coal from Newcastle, cheeses from Cheshire, herds of geese that the drover told me had waddled all the way from Norfolk. I saw people drinking cider from Devonshire and eating bacon from Gloucestershire. It smelt really sizzly.

I saw a Welshman with cattle that were as black as coal. I saw salmon on a stall that a sign said had been caught in the river Severn and in the river Trent. The stallholder said that these were rivers hundreds of miles away. The fish smelt good anyway.

There was a lot of noise and a lot of smells. I remembered our project on the five senses! I could smell things I don't really want to talk about. Put it like this, people didn't seem to bother to go to the lavatory: they just did what they had to do out there on the street and of course you couldn't expect the animals, the horses and the cows and suchlike, to go to a lavatory if you see what I mean. It was everywhere!

London in 1688 was just about the "five-sensiest" place you could be!

When we got into the court the English greeted William like a long-lost friend until his wife appeared. When Mary came into the room they all ran over to her and started bowing and scraping to her and saying things like, "Your Highness, your Highness, can we offer you the English crown?"—as if it were a bit of soda-bread or a wheaten farl or a wee bit of fruit-cake with butter on. "How would you like to be queen of England?" they asked again.

"I am hungry," Mary said. "I don't make decisions on an empty stomach. What you bring me to eat will help me decide." She winked at her husband.

They rushed off and brought her a huge pork pie and some cheese and biscuits to eat and white wine to drink. She said, "I wish to talk to my husband, alone."

William joined her. The two talked together. Once they laughed. When the courtiers heard that one laugh they all laughed too although they couldn't hear what William and Mary were saying. When William and Mary stopped laughing all the courtiers stopped laughing too. It was pathetic.

Then William came back into the centre of the room and said, "Mary's sister has refused the crown and I will not be consort to my wife. I will not rule England with my hands full of apron strings." Mary laughed. Everyone laughed. Mary stopped laughing. Everyone was silent.

The courtiers now offered William the English crown. They offered him wine as well. He refused it, shouting, "Bring me beer, ale for an honest man! Let the court drink ale!"

They brought in barrels of beer and tankards. Now they offered William food. Over ham and turkey and good old English ale again they offered him their England's crown.

They offered their English crown to a Dutchman and to a Protestant. He accepted it and Mary was given her crown too.

I rubbed the stone eye of the basilisk and all in front of me disappeared. I wanted at least one part of my story to have a happy ending. Does laughter always mean happiness?

Chapter 9

(In Ireland: the battlefield.)

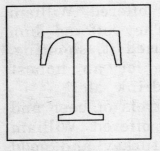

here was a lot of bad news in Belfast over the next few days. A lot of people were killed. I could hear my parents talking about it and Mr Redman, on his way into the classroom, would often be talking to the other teachers and looking serious. We, the children, just kept our heads down, kept very quiet and got on with our work and never looked up. I yearned to get away from it all.

The next time I climbed down the steps I was in London again, in the palace, with the courtiers—and there was William about to go into a meeting. When he saw me he waved me across and I stood beside him.

He said, "Do you know the way to Belfast?"

"I do surely," I said, "sure I live there."

The king laughed and laughed. I think he thought I was some kind of eedjit or something but I knew he enjoyed my company, although he did seem to humour me.

"Well, how do we get there then?" he asked.

"Well, if I was you," says I, "I would head off west through Wales and then sail north and land at Carrickfergus and then on up to Belfast. I mean that's your best bet because they're all Prods, all the way from Carrickfergus on." I was quite glad of the national curriculum at that point because before that Wales or England would have been a wave of Mr Redman's arm.

"Thank you, child," said the King and then he went on, "but if I were to say to you King James is in Kinsale and Dublin gathering an army of Catholics to march north what would you say to that?"

"Gather your own army up in Belfast and march south," I said, "Who's got the most men?"

"*We* will have," said the king, "by a long chalk!"

"Well, then," I said, "get down there and get stuck in!"

The king laughed. "Good," he said.

Then he mused for a while and asked me again, "And meet James where?"

"At Drogheda," I said.

"Drogheda?" said the king. "Never heard of it! But no matter, Drogheda you say?"

I was really enjoying this, giving a king advice, especially since I knew he would have to follow it because I knew the story in the future from our project and things my da had told me.

William, of course, had no idea what was going to be or even who would win. That was why he kept saying quite often, "What will be will be."

"There's a river running there," I said, "flowing roughly west to east.

It cuts the country in two. James will have to cross it coming north from Dublin: that's where to meet with him. The river is called the Boyne."

"Splendid, child," said the king. "I'll go now and see what my advisers say. You slip in quietly and duke down at the back and we'll compare notes afterwards."

The king swept into his council chamber with all his ministers and experts and I slipped in after them like a wee wee mouse.

The ministers all had maps and at last they worked out a route and a battle-plan. "We will go," said the chief expert, "to the place called Carrick-the-Fergus and then to the town called the Bell-fast. Then we turn to the south and march towards Dublin and meet the forces of King James somewhere along the way."

"Maybe at the Drogheda?" said the king politely.

His advisers searched their maps for a place called Drogheda and when they found it they said, "What a brilliant idea, Your Majesty, just the spot. There is a river, the Boyne; we can meet on the banks, they to the south, and we to the north. What a splendid idea, sire."

"Thank you," said the King, well pleased. I knew now I was well in.

❖

When we landed at Carrick the king had already thousands of men with him and we gathered up more in Belfast. "When shall we leave?" asked one of the generals.

"We leave now," said King William. "I have not come to Ireland to let the grass grow under my feet!" The war had begun.

When we got to the north bank of the Boyne we could see James's army waiting on the south bank. There was a wee bridge up to the east and we all thought that whoever held the bridge might win the battle. But then I had another thought—suppose the battle could be fought in the river itself: that would be when the river would flow red with the blood of Irishmen and Ulstermen. The blood of Catholic and Protestant would be one in death.

William could see that I was sad and when he asked me what was wrong I poured out my heart to him, I said that here on one bank of the Boyne were Protestants, on the other bank there were Catholics and that only when we were all dead and in the river floating away would the argument be over. I said that the blood that would flow in the river would be Catholic blood and Protestant blood but that neither river nor sea would be able to tell the difference.

The King was touched by my speech and he walked with me to the little bridge and there he sat down and took a crumpled piece of paper out of his pocket. "Last night I wrote a poem," he said. "I've shown it to no one, I don't know whether it's any good or not but you can have a read of it."

I opened up the crumpled paper and this is what I read:

My View of Myself
by William of Orange

As I walked by myself
And talk'd to myself,
My self said unto me,
Look to thyself,
For nobody cares for thee.

I answered myself
And said to myself,
In the self-same repartee,
Look to thyself
Or not look to thyself
The self same thing will be.
                              William III

"Sweet," I said. "Really sweet."

At that moment a bullet came flying across the river and hit the King in the shoulder. He fell and was bleeding badly. I helped him up—we were both about the same size—and he was mopping the wound with his handkerchief. I helped him.

We hobbled to his camp and his soldiers and he demanded of them that they raise him onto his favourite white horse. Sitting there uncertainly he managed to get his sword out of its scabbard and now raised it painfully up over his shoulder. He shouted, "What are the men of Enniskillen to do for me today? What are my brave Huguenots to do for me today? Of all my soldiers I ask, what are you to do for me today?" As answer to each question, William received a cheer. Plunging into the water he led the attack on James.

During the battle I swam and scrambled ashore on the other side and saw this really nice old man whom I thought I recognised. He was sitting in the midst of the fighting crying or at least that's what I thought first. In fact he had a nose-bleed and was mopping the blood running from his nostrils with his handkerchief. I helped him and he was kind and grateful. Then I recognised him from England and it suddenly seemed oh, so long ago. I recognised him from the fishing boats and the tangy English air and realised he was the other king, James. He didn't recognise me but thanked

me for my help and said, "I have no
stomach for this battle today. I just
want to go home." I felt like saying,
"You had your chance two years ago
when Willy put you on that wee
fishing boat," but I held my tongue.

The last I saw of him he was
heading off with what was left of his
army toward Dublin, Cork or Kinsale
and then I suppose to France and
Catholic safety. William marched on
to Dublin. Now Ireland and England
would be Protestant countries, just as
they had once been Catholic ones.

On my way back up the secret
steps I found a wine glass. On it were
engraved the words, *God Bless Wilyam.*
I thought it would make a nice
souvenir or least be an artefact or
exhibit for our science table.

I did not know then that I was
going to climb down the stone steps
only once again...

Part V
The Lost City of Belfast

Denise '91

Chapter 10

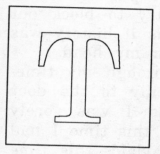

he simurgh which dwells high in the Persian mountains is a large and beautiful bird with a dog's head. It has orange feathers that shine like burnished copper, the talons of a vulture and a tail like a peacock's. The simurgh nests in the Tree of Knowledge and is the wisest of all birds. It speaks all languages and can tell what has been, what is and what is to be. It was this visitor to our shores that I met on my last descent.

On that descent I passed the door to the Siege of Derry, to the Battle of the Boyne, went on down and down passing many doors of history.

I thought a lot about my adventures, about the Protestant and Catholic thing. It was all Catholic and Protestant, Protestant and Catholic, and not just in Ireland. I put my hands around my ears to try to block out the conflict. It was as if history was arguing with itself in my head.

As I walked on through my timetunnel I came suddenly to the door of Saint Patrick and I was sorely tempted to go in but this time I had decided not to be waylaid, this time I had decided to go on and on until I came to the very end—or do I mean the very beginning?

After Saint Patrick it got dark and cold and somehow ancient, and I felt I was going towards something dangerous, even unknown. Music began to sound, a kind of humming like an Enya tape. At the end of my tunnel was a tiny wooden door that looked as if it had been made from an old rotting boat. On it was written one word, *Banba*. I was just about to push it and go in when this simurgh bird appeared.

The bird was very tall and grand and had a posh accent. It said, "Before you enter there, my child, I would like you to consider the following proposition."

I asked the creature who or what it was and where was my cockatrice.

It explained all about itself, where it came from, what it could do and told me that I had passed far beyond the powers of the cockatrice or basilisk. It then posed me a question and forced me to make a choice, a choice upon which the rest of this story hangs.

"If you open this door," the simurgh bird said, "you will enter and learn of the beginning of Ireland's past. How it all began."

The bird then stood aside and I saw it had been guarding another door. "If you enter this door," the giant bird said, "you come into the Future."

I couldn't wait. I shouted, "The Future, the Future!" And I barged through the door.

The future was green, the light was

green. I could see the City Hall. It was in ruins like the Parthenon in Athens: it was really crumbling so I knew I must be eons into the future. Then I felt this tugging at my cardigan and the big bird pulled me back out from the entrance with one of its talons. "Silly child," the bird said, "you didn't let me finish my sentence."

"Sorry," I said, "what's the problem?"

"Problem?" said the bird. "Simply this, child. I offered you a choice but you didn't give me time to tell of the strings attached."

"Strings attached?" I said. "What strings?"

"Just this," said the simurgh bird. "I offered you a choice between history and the future. What you didn't give me time to tell you was that if you choose the future, sure you can go there but you can't *ever* come back!"

"What, never get back to Belfast?"

"Never!" said the Persian brain-machine.

"Oh well, then," I said, "that's no problem, I choose history, I want to go and meet Banba."

"It's too late," said the simurgh bird. "Other strings attached say that you have only *one* choice. You can't choose one thing and then have it granted, and then change your mind and say you'll have the other. You chose the Future, and barged through the door. I could have left you there. In a way I suppose I have saved your life."

"Thank you," I said humbly. Then I said, "Tell me great simurgh bird, is it true that you can tell the future and the present and the past?"

The bird puffed up its feathers proudly and said, "Yes."

"Well then," I said, "maybe you can *tell* me what is to happen to Belfast and to Ireland?"

I could see the bird liked me, probably because I had been flattering it. "Now," it said, "you may take a feather from my right wing, child—that is my wing of the future. That one feather will tell you one thing."

I carefully plucked a feather from the right wing of the simurgh bird and then it whispered in my ear, "Belfast is in great danger, so is

Ireland." I listened very attentively. "If the people of Ireland and Britain keep on destroying the ozone layer, a terrible storm will blow in space and the earth will tilt ever so slightly on its axis and Ireland and Belfast will fall off the map of the world."

"Oh, heavens above!" I said, "we can't have that happening."

The simurgh bird suddenly looked exhausted as if the parting from its feather and the giving away of the information had been very difficult for it. Even so, it now said, "As a souvenir, pluck a feather from the left wing, that is my wing of the past. Take it home with you and place it on your history table at school. It will bring you good luck."

I bade the bird farewell and started my long climb back to my own civilisation. As you can imagine I was sad because my adventures were over.

That night I watched the swans circle the waterworks and then land in a great spray. I thought of my mythical friends, the basilisk and the simurgh bird. I thought of all the real people I had met. The late sunlight made the swans' spray look magical. In it I could see everything, over and over again.

The next day I placed the feather from the right wing of the simurgh bird on the science table and the feather from its left wing on the history table.

That day I made sure I was the last to leave the classroom. At the door I turned round once to have a final look. The whole classroom seemed to shimmer.

The End

Author's Note

This story was inspired by something I read in the *Guardian* back in the summer of 1987. According to the article a Mrs Lorna Chatfield (then sixty-one) had, at the age of twelve, been poking about and digging at the bottom of her garden when she chanced upon a Roman palace. This was later identified as having first been built for King Cogidubnus circa AD 75. The reason she had been digging was that she had been doing a project on the Romans at school. She found the palace about a foot under the ground.

Sadly, however, she wasn't allowed to tell anyone because the neighbours said they didn't want a lot of archaeologists poking about the place upsetting the cows. So for forty-nine years she kept the secret because, as she said, "In those days children did what they were told."

She decided to reveal the secret only when the family house was to be sold. It was a major archaeological find.

In transferring the story to Ireland and Belfast I am indebted to the following authors and publications:

The Oxford History of England, Sir George Clark.

"The Narrow Ground", A.T.Q. Stewart, *Apollo*, Vol 3, 1926

Seven Kings of England, Geoffrey Trease

English History in Verse, Kenneth Baker

The Siege of Derry, J.G. Simms

Prose, Poems and Parodies of Percy French (Talbot Press)

Fabulous Beasts, Monika Beisner/Alison Lurie

Also to Christy Moore whose great songs I was playing in the background almost throughout.

I also wish to acknowledge the peace and order I found at Mount Pleasant in Reigate, the retreat where this book was written.

Children's Poolbeg Books

Author	Title	ISBN	Price
Banville Vincent	Hennessy	1 85371 132 2	£3.99
Beckett Mary	Orla was Six	1 85371 047 4	£2.99
Beckett Mary	Orla at School	1 85371 157 8	£2.99
Comyns Michael	The Trouble with Marrows	1 85371 117 9	£3.99
Considine June	When the Luvenders came to Merrick Town	1 85371 055 5	£4.50
Considine June	Luvenders at the Old Mill	1 85371 115 2	£4.50
Considine June	Island of Luvenders	1 85371 149 7	£4.50
Corcoran Clodagh ed.	Baker's Dozen	1 85371 050 4	£3.50
Corcoran Clodagh ed.	Discoveries	1 85371 019 9	£4.99
Cruickshank Margrit	SKUNK and the Ozone Conspiracy	1 85371 067 9	£3.99
Cruickshank Margrit	SKUNK and the Splitting Earth	1 85371 119 5	£3.99
Daly Ita	Candy on the DART	1 85371 057 1	£2.99
Daly Ita	Candy and Sharon Olé	1 85371 159 4	£3.50
Dillon Eilís	The Seekers	1 85371 152 7	£3.50
Dillon Eilís	The Singing Cave	1 85371 153 5	£3.99
Duffy Robert	Children's Quizbook No.1	1 85371 020 2	£2.99
Duffy Robert	Children's Quizbook No.2	1 85371 052 0	£2.99
Duffy Robert	Children's Quizbook No.3	1 85371 099 7	£2.99
Duffy Robert	The Euroquiz Book	1 85371 151 9	£3.50
Ellis Brendan	Santa and the King of Starless Nights	1 85371 114 4	£2.99
Henning Ann	The Connemara Whirlwind	1 85371 079 2	£3.99
Henning Ann	The Connemara Stallion	1 85371 158 6	£3.99
Hickey Tony	Blanketland	1 85371 043 1	£2.99
Hickey Tony	Foodland	1 85371 075 X	£2.99
Hickey Tony	Legendland	1 85371 122 5	£3.50
Hickey Tony	Where is Joe?	1 85371 045 8	£3.99
Hickey Tony	Joe in the Middle	1 85371 021 0	£3.99
Hickey Tony	Joe on Holiday	1 85371 145 4	£3.50
Hickey Tony	Spike & the Professor	1 85371 039 3	£2.99
Hickey Tony	Spike and the Professor and Doreen at the Races	1 85371 089 X	£3.50
Hickey Tony	Spike, the Professor and Doreen in London	1 85371 130 6	£3.99
Kelly Eamon	The Bridge of Feathers	1 85371 053 9	£2.99
Lavin Mary	A Likely Story	1 85371 104 7	£2.99
Lynch Patricia	Brogeen and the Green Shoes	1 85371 051 2	£3.50
Lynch Patricia	Brogeen follows the Magic Tune	1 85371 022 9	£2.99
Lynch Patricia	Sally from Cork	1 85371 070 9	£3.99
Lynch Patricia	The Turfcutter's Donkey	1 85371 016 4	£3.99
MacMahon Bryan	Patsy-O	1 85371 036 9	£3.50
McCann Sean	Growing Things	1 85371 029 6	£2.99
McMahon Sean	The Poolbeg Book of Children's Verse	1 85371 080 6	£4.99
McMahon Sean	Shoes and Ships and Sealing Wax	1 85371 046 6	£2.99
McMahon Sean	The Light on Illancrone	1 85371 083 0	£3.50
McMahon Sean	The Three Seals	1 85371 148 9	£3.99
Mullen Michael	The Viking Princess	1 85371 015 6	£2.99
Mullen Michael	The Caravan	1 85371 074 1	£2.99
Mullen Michael	The Little Drummer Boy	1 85371 035 0	£2.99
Mullen Michael	The Long March	1 85371 109 8	£3.50
Mullen Michael	The Flight of the Earls	1 85371 146 2	£3.99
Ní Dhuibhne Eilís	The Uncommon Cormorant	1 85371 111 X	£2.99

Author	Title	ISBN	Price
Ní Dhuibhne Eilís	Hugo and the Sunshine Girl	1 85371 160 8	£3.50
Ó hEithir Breandán	An Nollaig Thiar	1 85371 044 X	£2.99
Ó Faoláin Eileen	The Little Black Hen	1 85371 049 0	£2.99
Ó Faoláin Eileen	Children of the Salmon	1 85371 003 2	£3.99
Ó Faoláin Eileen	Irish Sagas and Folk Tales	0 90516 971 9	£3.95
Quarton Marjorie	The Cow Watched the Battle	1 85371 084 9	£2.99
Quarton Marjorie	The Other Side of the Island	1 85371 161 6	£3.50
Quinn John	The Summer of Lily and Esme	1 85371 162 4	£3.99
Ross Gaby	Damien the Dragon	1 85371 078 4	£2.99
Schulman Anne	Children's Book of Puzzles	1 85371 133 0	£3.99
Snell Gordon	Cruncher Sparrow High Flier	1 85371 100 4	£2.99
Snell Gordon	Cruncher Sparrow's Flying School	1 85371 163 2	£2.99
Stanley-Higel Mary	Poolbeg Book of Children's Crosswords 1	1 85371 098 9	£2.99
Stanley-Higel Mary	Poolbeg Book of Children's Crosswords 2	1 85371 150 0	£3.50
Swift Carolyn	Bugsy Goes to Cork	1 85371 071 7	£3.50
Swift Carolyn	Bugsy Goes to Limerick	1 85371 014 8	£3.50
Swift Carolyn	Bugsy Goes to Galway	1 85371 147 0	£3.99
Swift Carolyn	Irish Myths and Tales	1 85371 103 9	£2.99
Swift Carolyn	Robbers on TV	1 85371 033 4	£2.99
Swift Carolyn	Robbers on the Streets	1 85371 113 6	£3.50
Traynor Shaun	A Little Man in England	1 85371 032 6	£2.99
Traynor Shaun	Hugo O'Huge	1 85371 048 2	£2.99
Traynor Shaun	The Giants' Olympics	1 85371 088 1	£2.99
Traynor Shaun	The Lost City of Belfast	1 85371 164 0	£3.50
	The Ultimate Children's Joke Book	1 85371 168 3	£2.99

While every effort is made to keep prices low, it is sometimes necessary to increase prices at short notice. Poolbeg Press Ltd reserves the right to show new retail prices on covers which may differ from those previously advertised in the text or elsewhere.

All Poolbeg books are available at your bookshop or newsagent or can be ordered from:

Poolbeg Press Knocksedan House
Forrest Great Swords Co Dublin
Tel: 01 407433 Fax: 01 403753

Please send a cheque or postal order (no currency) made payable to Poolbeg Press Ltd.

Allow 80p for postage for the first book, plus 50p for each additional book ordered.

Children's
POOLBEG

To get regular
information about
our books and authors join

THE POOLBEG
BOOK CLUB

To become a member of
THE POOLBEG BOOK CLUB
Write to Anne O'Reilly,
The Poolbeg Book Club,
Knocksedan House,
Swords, Co. Dublin.
Please write clearly and make sure to include
all the following details: Name, full address,
date of birth, school.